Think, Draw, Create!

This edition published by Parragon Books Ltd in 2016

Parragon Books Ltd
Chartist House
15–17 Trim Street
Bath BA1 1HA, UK
www.parragon.com

Written by Frances Prior-Reeves
Designed by Talking Design
Illustrations by Eleanor Carter

ISBN 978-1-4748-5033-9

Printed in China

Think, Draw, Create!

PaRragon

Bath • New York • Cologne • Melbourne • Delhi
Hong Kong • Shenzhen • Singapore

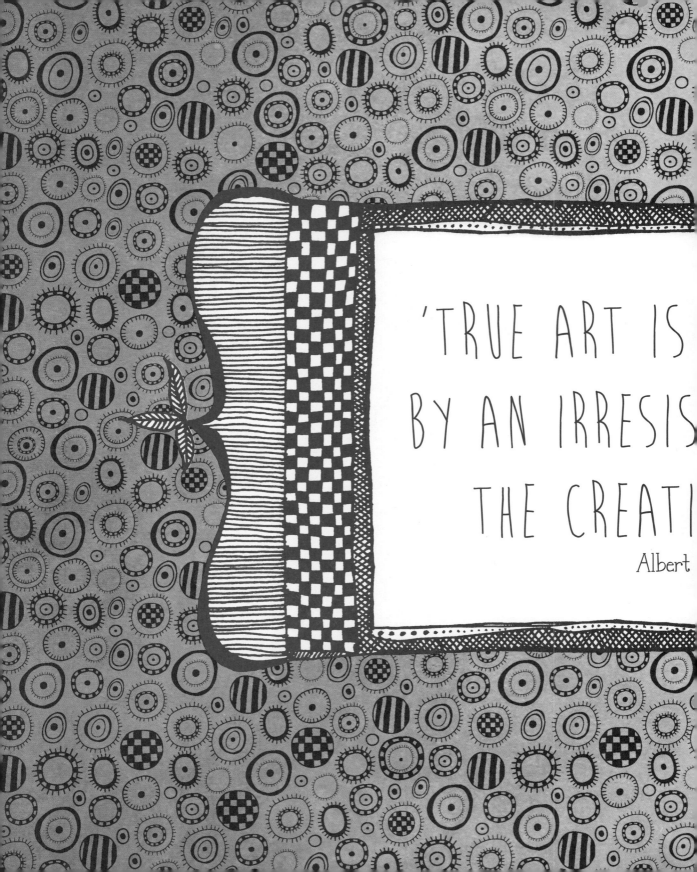

'TRUE ART IS
BY AN IRRESIS
THE CREATI
Albert

CHARACTERIZED
TIBLE URGE IN
VE ARTIST.'

Einstein

Draw the future in this
crystal ball.

Draw this
frog's croak.

Draw something **hot**.

Nandos
~~chicken~~
Peri-Peri

Fire pit

Ice-cube

snow flake.

Draw something cold.

Unlock this box.

Meep

Draw what is **INSIDE.**

Fill this page with *teardrops*.

Can you transform
those teardrops into a *fire?*

Fill this pattern with as much colour as possible.

Add flames to these candles.

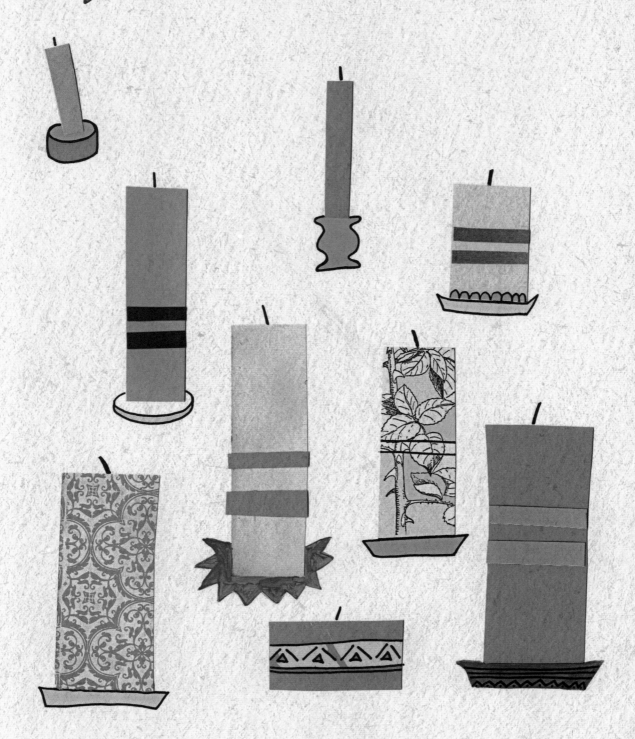

Draw a **timeline** of your day.

Draw what comes out at *night.*

Draw a self-portrait in a **pop-art style.**

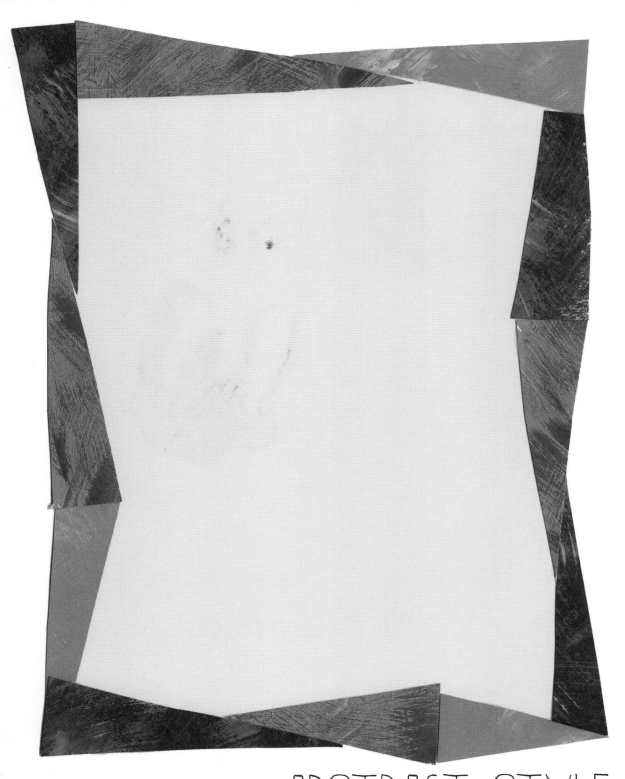

Draw a self-portrait in an ABSTRACT STYLE.

Draw **ORANGE**
ignoring red.

Draw *blue* submerged
in yellow.

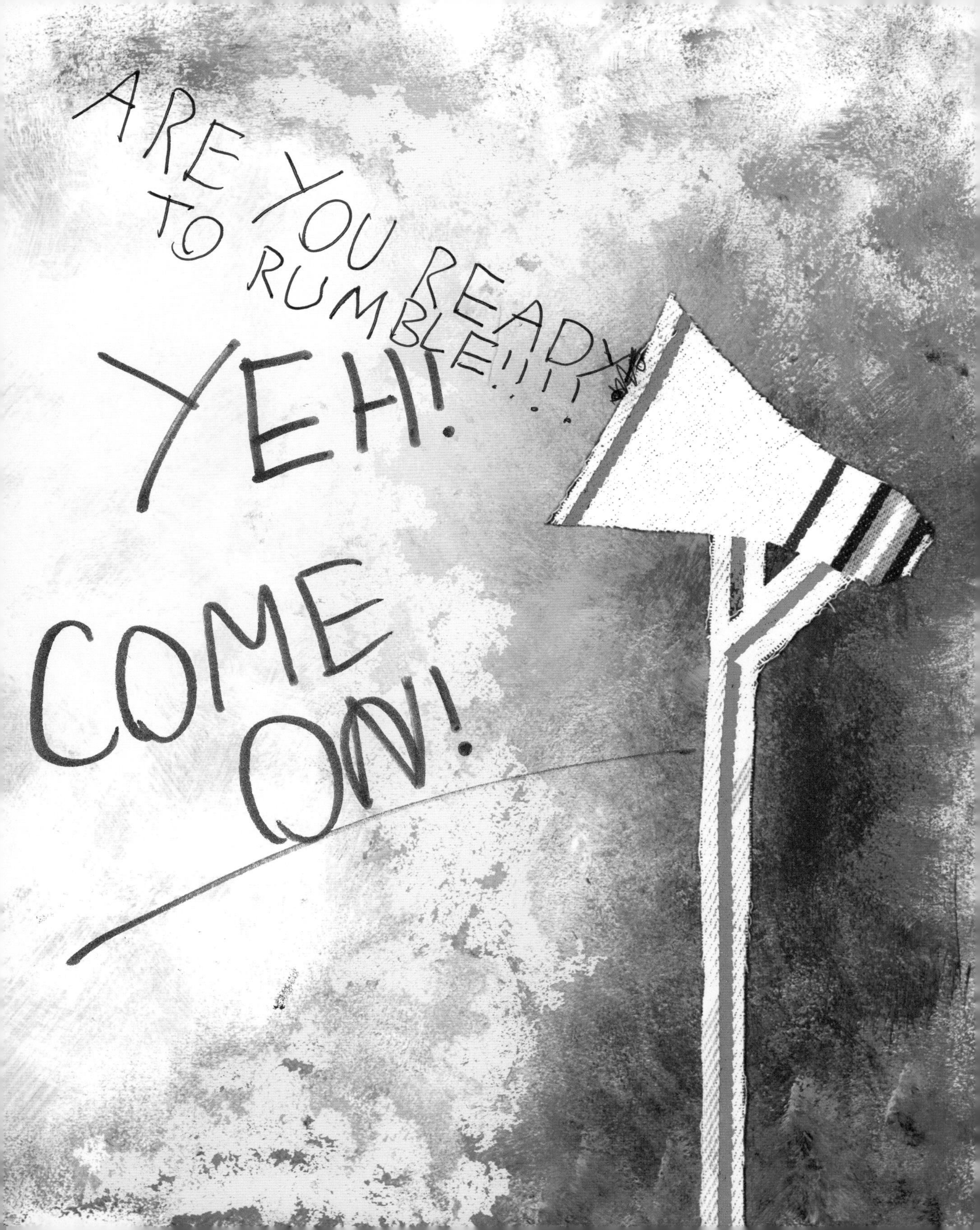
ARE YOU READY TO RUMBLE!!!!
YEH!
COME ON!

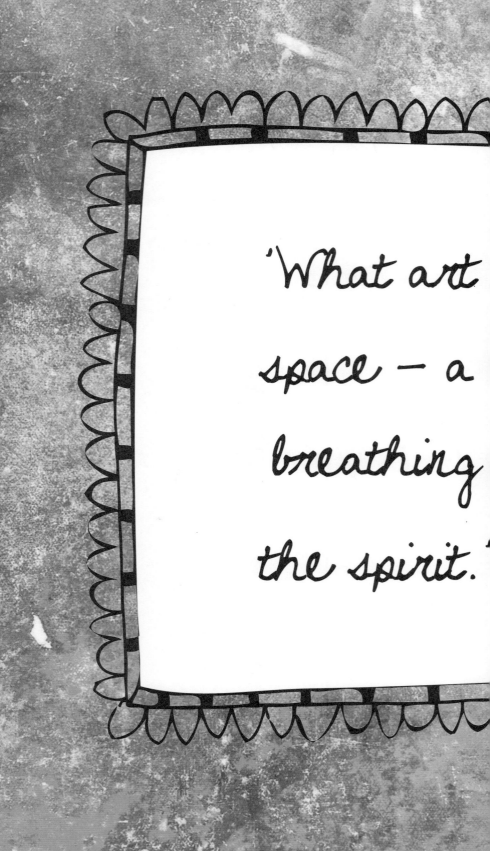

'What art

space — a

breathing

the spirit.'

offers is

certain

room for

John Updike

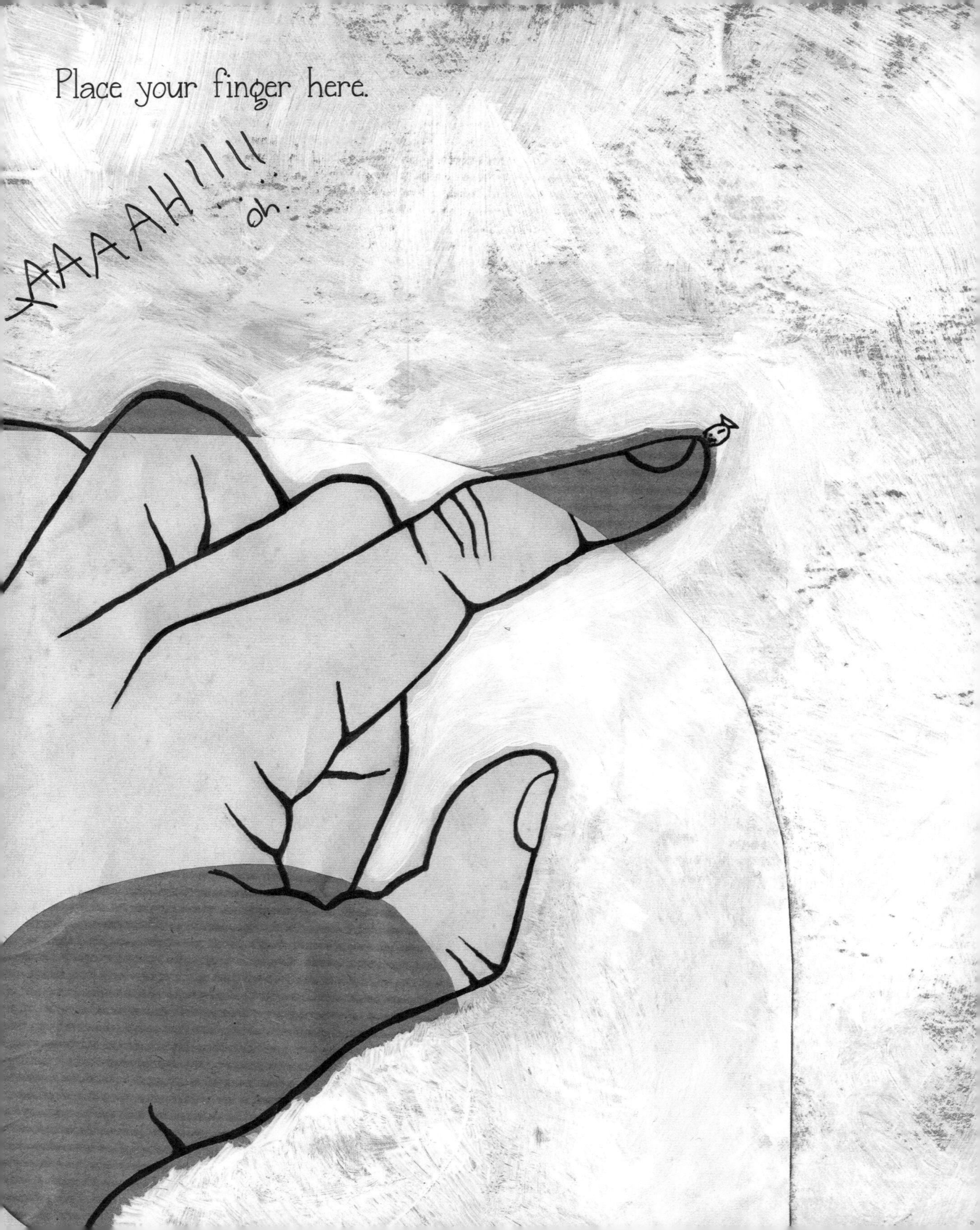
Place your finger here.
AAAAH!!!!!
oh.

Now draw something **BITING** it.

DON'T RESTRICT YOURSELF.

Draw your **favourite film.**

Nativity

Draw your *least favourite film.*

Draw your **INVENTION.**

create

MAKE

PRACTICE

do

draw

PAINT

sketch

FIND

inspire

COPY

Draw a *bear* that is late.

Draw a **TREE**.

Draw the same tree
but far away on
this *hilltop.*

DRAW ANYTHING!

Add people under these umbrellas.

Draw your
daydream.

Using this graph paper, design a pattern
using colours that gradually get brighter.

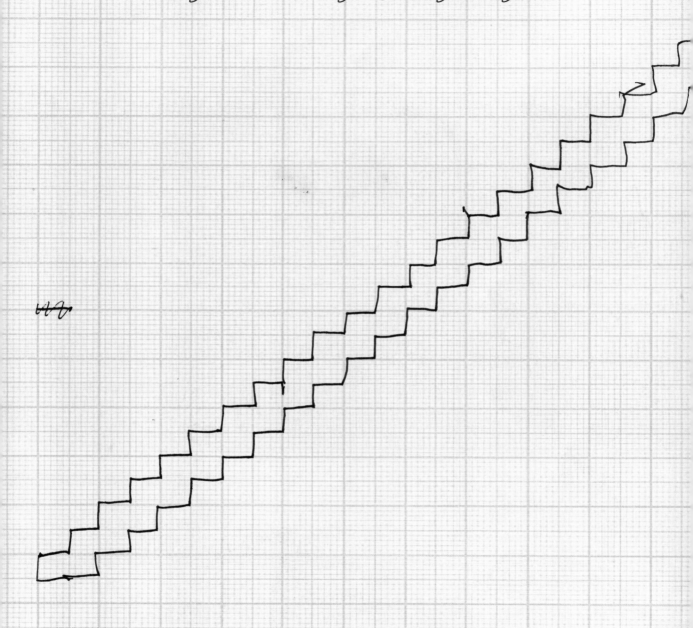

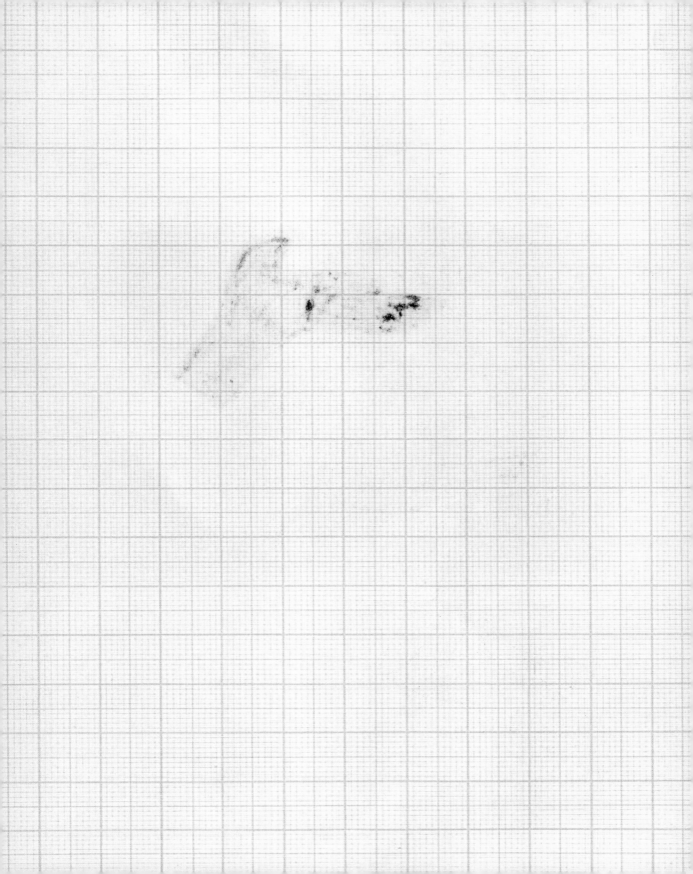

Draw hands making
shadow puppets.

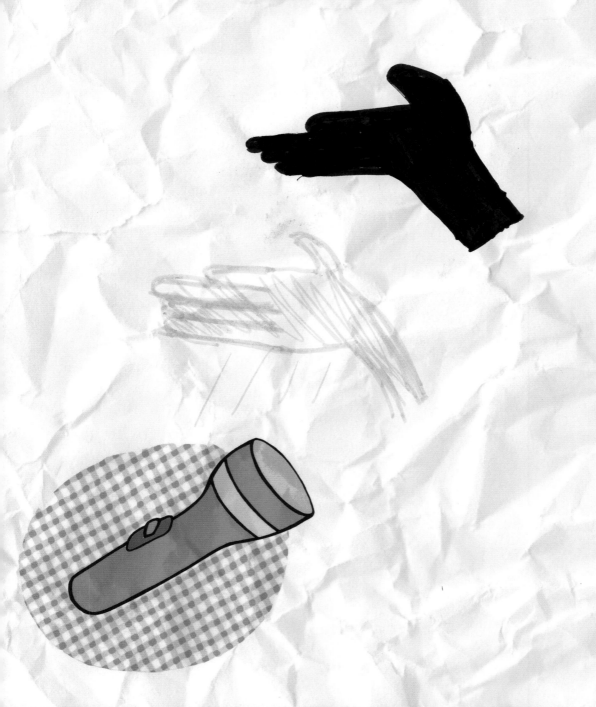

Draw the view from your window in
BLACK AND WHITE.

Now draw the same view
using colour,
but no outlines.

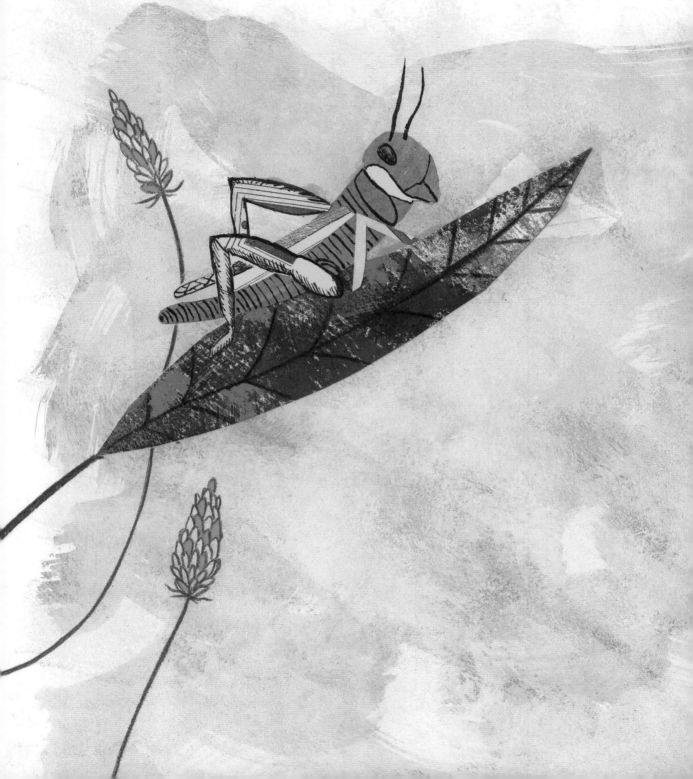

Draw this **grasshopper's chirp.**

Add BODIES to these arms.

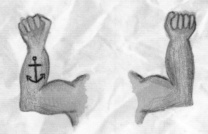

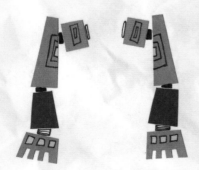

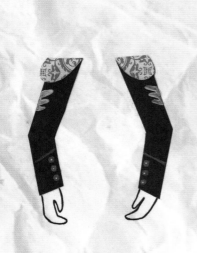

DON'T THINK, JUST CREATE!

Draw something CURVY.

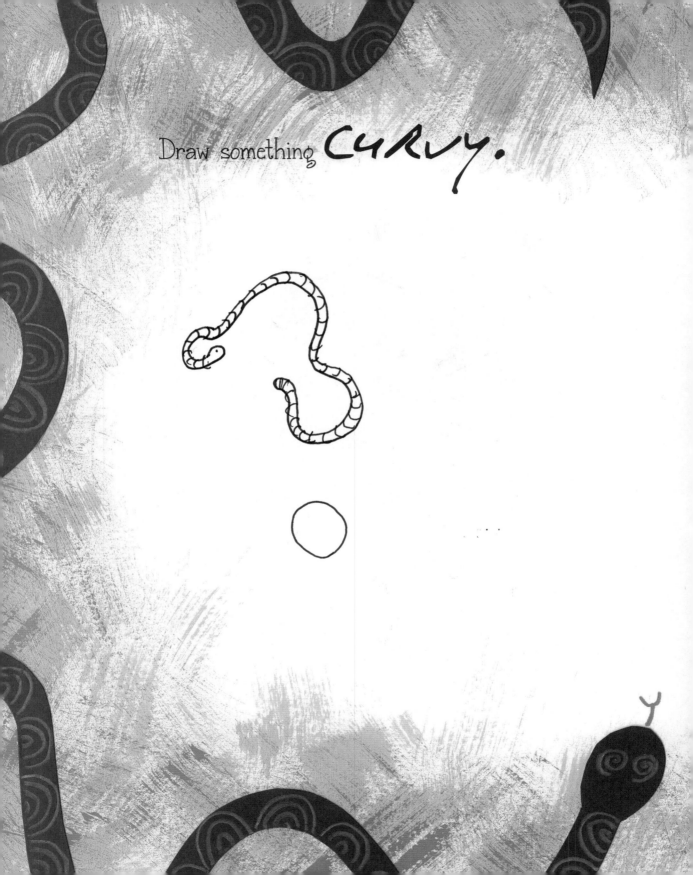

Circle

Draw the same thing using only
STRAIGHT LINES.

Design a book cover for a **SPY NOVEL.**

Design a book cover for a *fairy tale.*

Draw a creature

that is made up of your three favourite animals.

| Eagle | Owl | Dolphin |

The Ewlphin

Rhino kitten Fox

The Rhittox

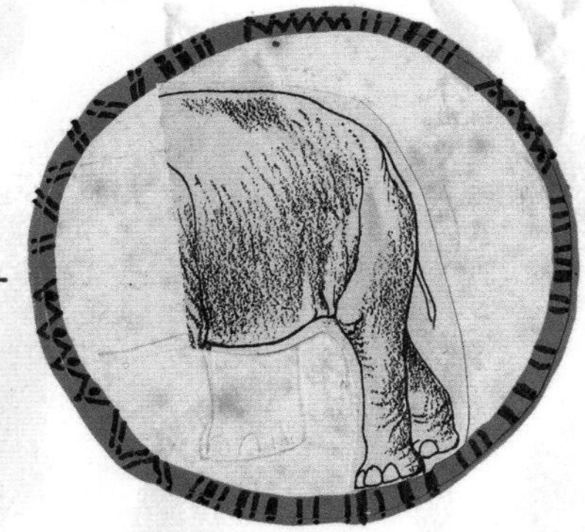

Draw a WISH.

Draw something *young.*

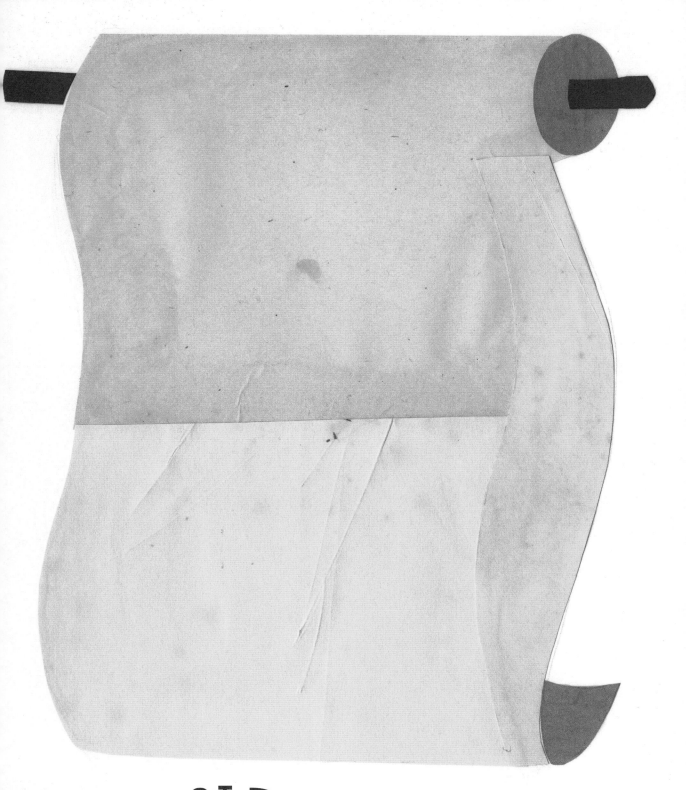

Draw something OLD.

Draw something **melting.**

'By striving to do man has always achieved what cautiously done no more than never taken a single

Mikhail

the impossible,
is possible. Those who have
they believed possible have
step forward.'

Bakunin

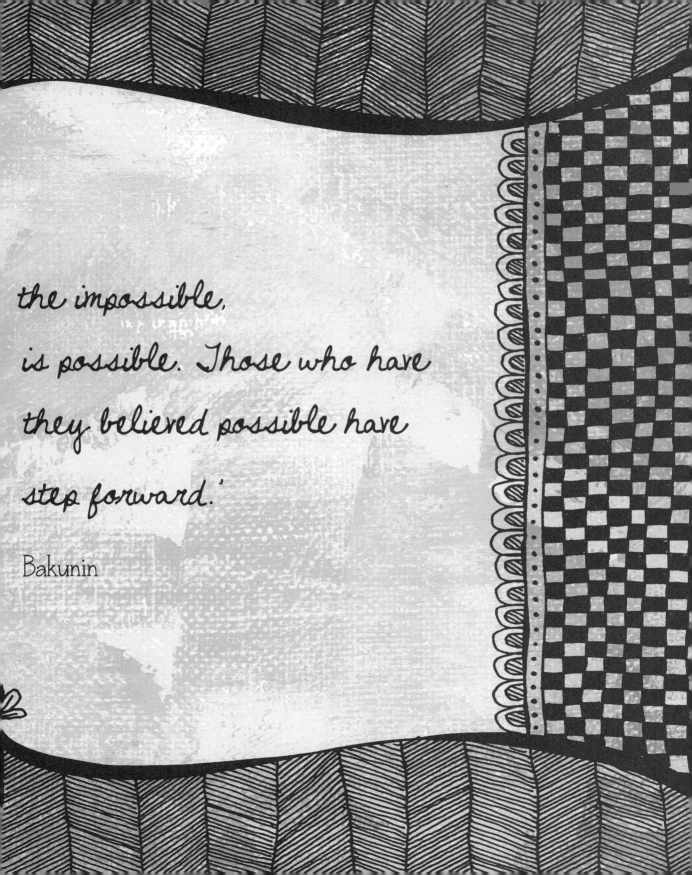

Draw cream *cursing brown.*

Draw green ADMIRING TEAL.

Draw purple

confronting pink.

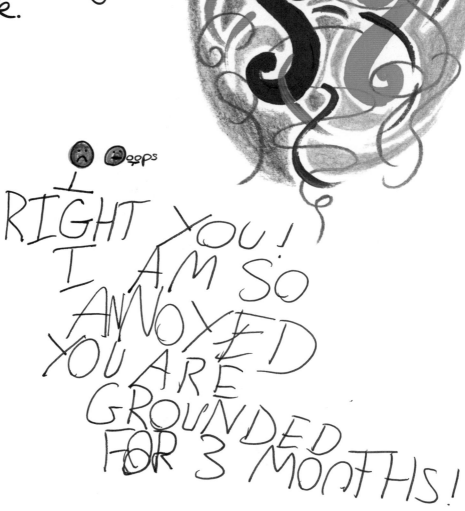

RIGHT YOU!
I AM SO
ANNOYED
YOU ARE
GROUNDED
FOR 3 MONTHS!

Draw a **FLYING PANDA**.

Draw a
huggable lizard.

Draw a *joke*.

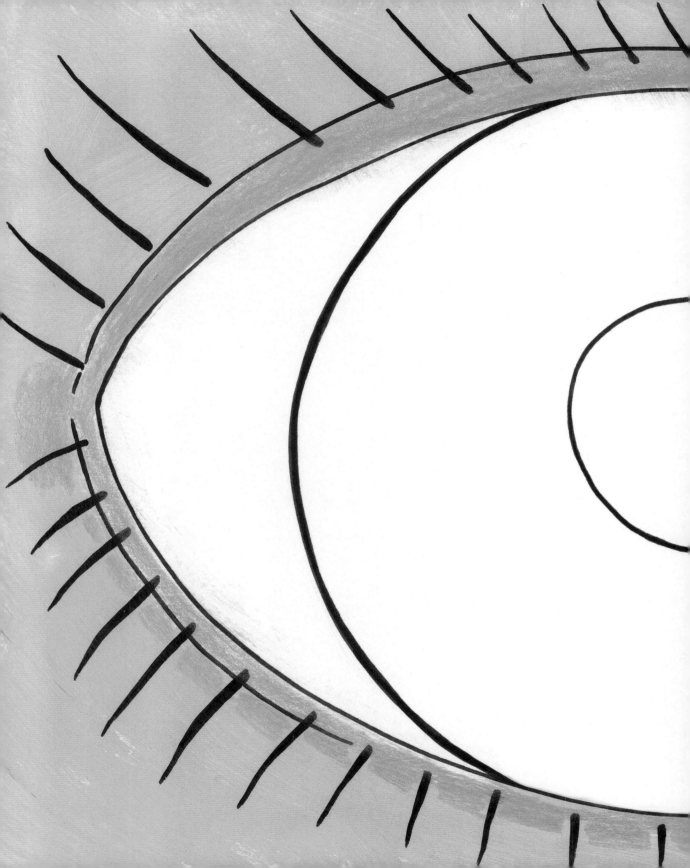

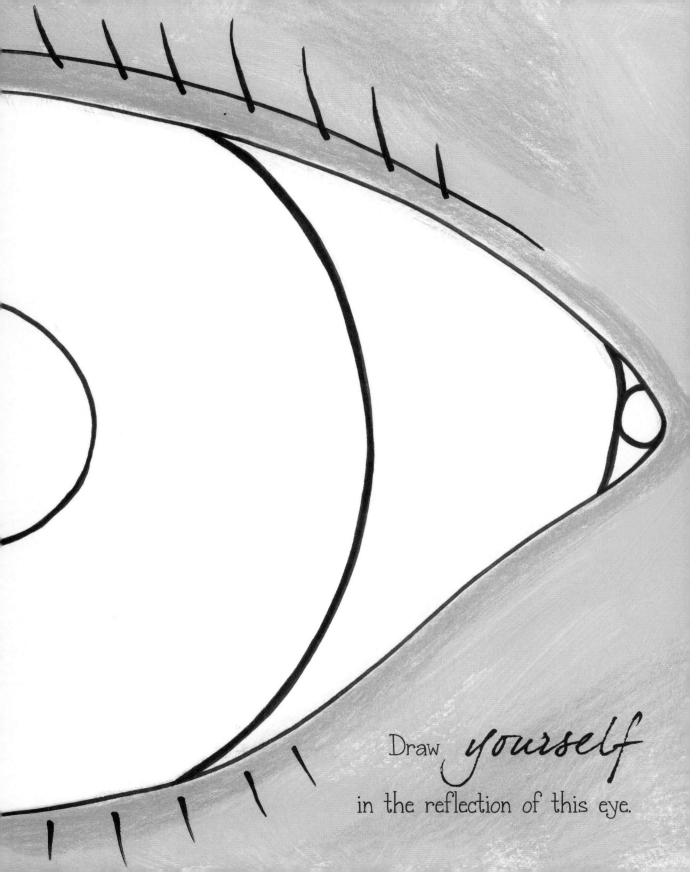

Draw *yourself* in the reflection of this eye.

Using this graph paper,
create a **MAP TO YOUR
TREASURE.**

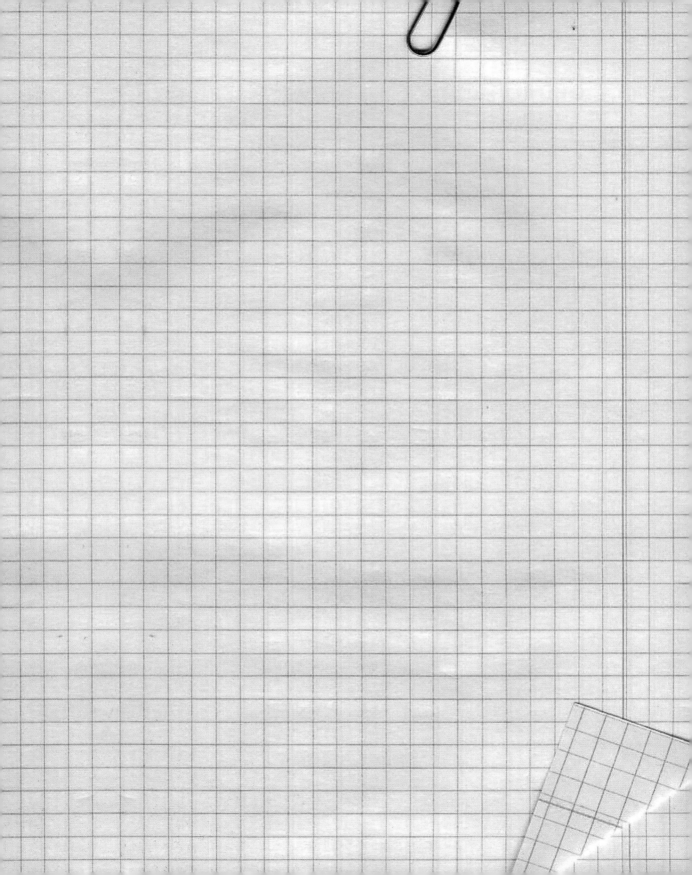

Emptiness is conceptually for sheer nothingness of infinite

D. T.

which

liable to be mistaken
is in fact the reservoir

possibilities.'

Suzuki

Transform *the* *emptiness.*

Draw a *snowball fight*.

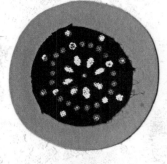

Draw something you want **right now**.

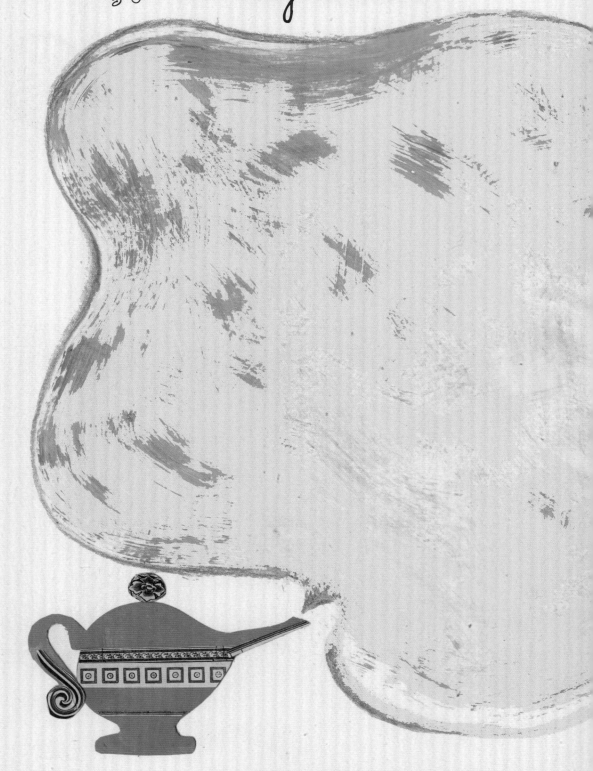

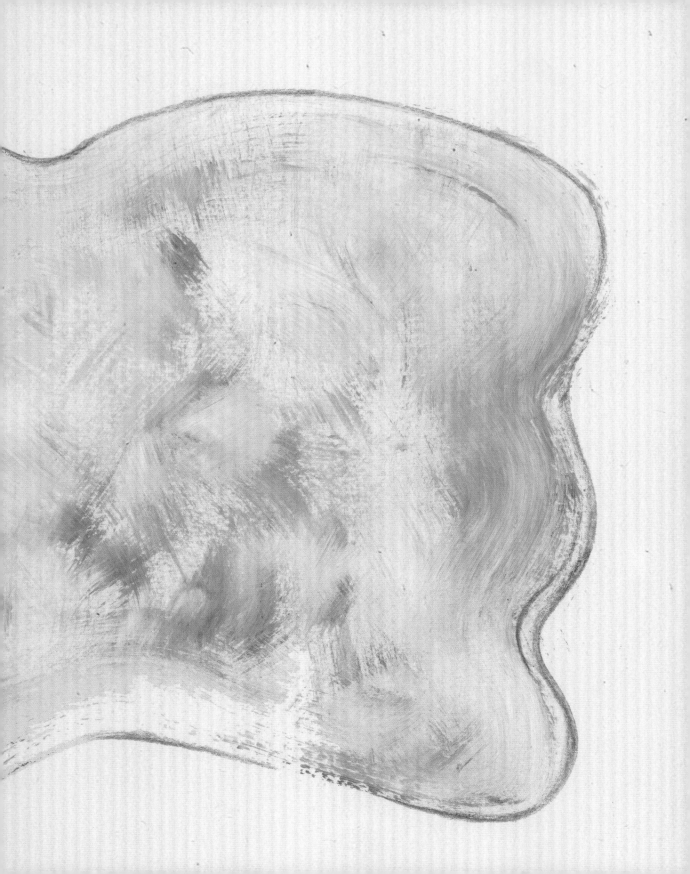

Draw **things flying**
that usually can't.

PICK UP
A PENCIL.

Fill these pages with
green creatures.

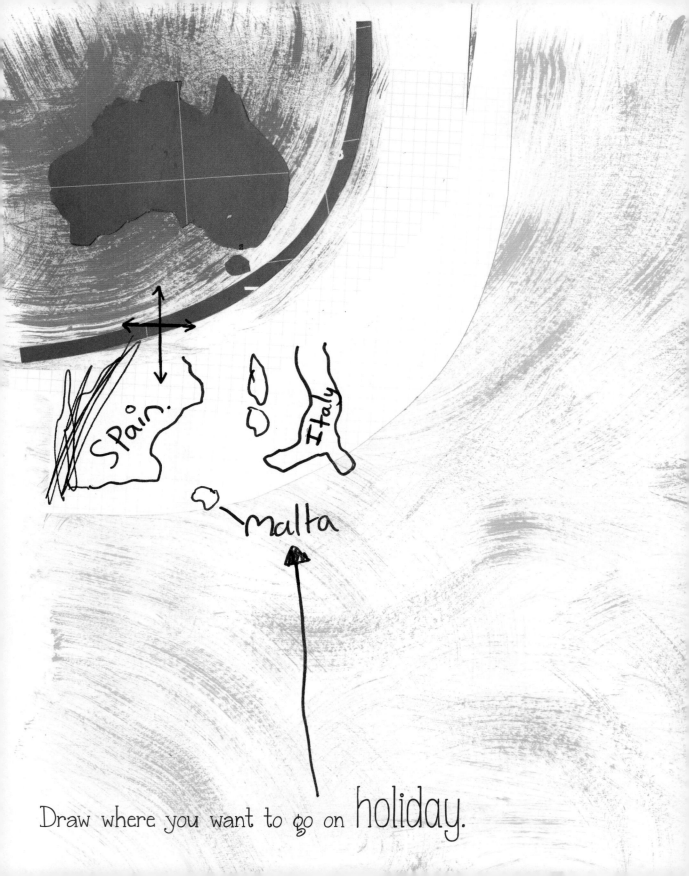

Spain.

Italy

Malta

Draw where you want to go on holiday.

Draw **HEAVY** things.

Draw LIGHT things.

Fill this page with as many **different** *colours* as you can.

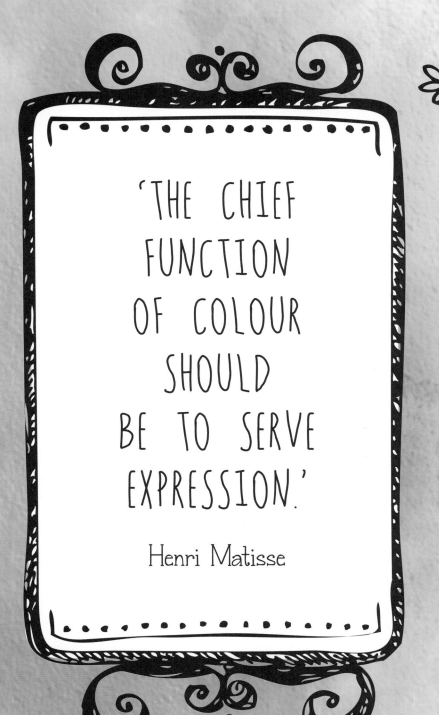

'THE CHIEF
FUNCTION
OF COLOUR
SHOULD
BE TO SERVE
EXPRESSION.'

Henri Matisse

Draw this *wolf's howl.*

Draw yourself angry.

Draw yourself **scared.**

possibilities

POSSIBILITIES

possibilities

possibilies

POSSIBILITIES

POSSIBILITIES

possibilities

POSSIBILITIES

possibilities

possibilities

POSSIBILITIES

possibilities

possibilities

Draw what is outside without taking your

PENCIL OFF THE PAGE.

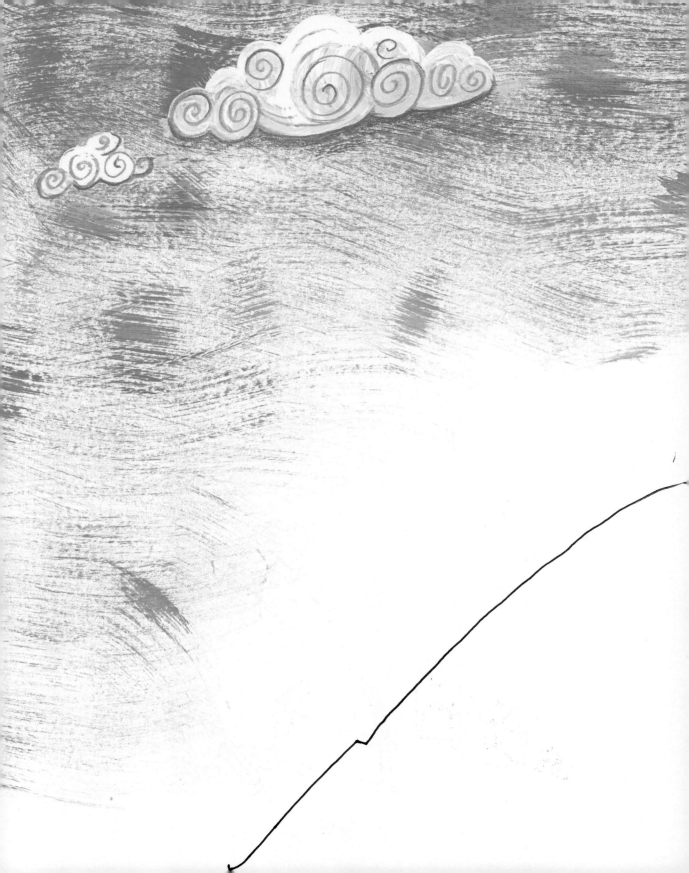

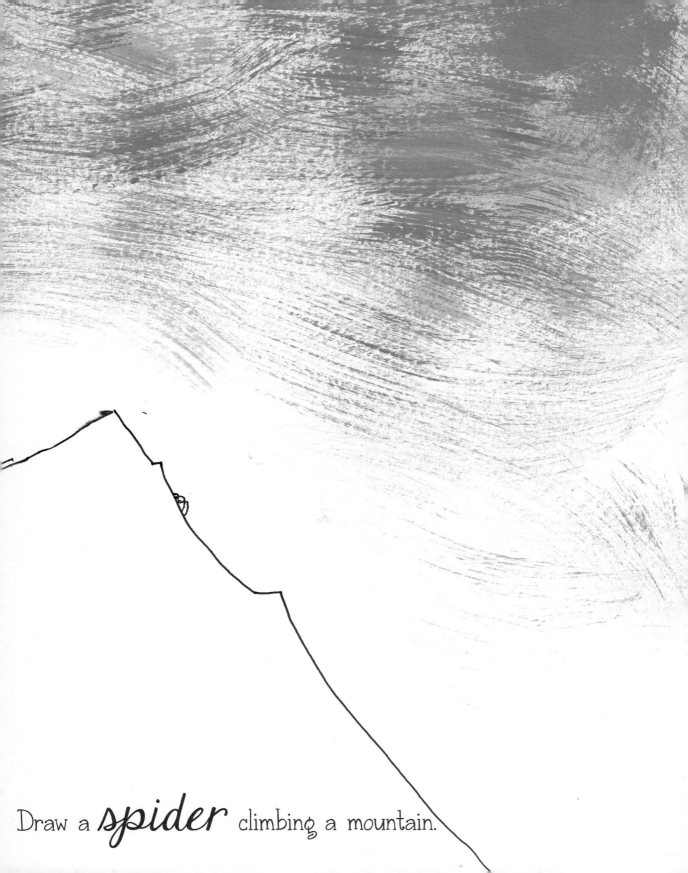

Draw a *spider* climbing a mountain.

SHADE ANYTHING!

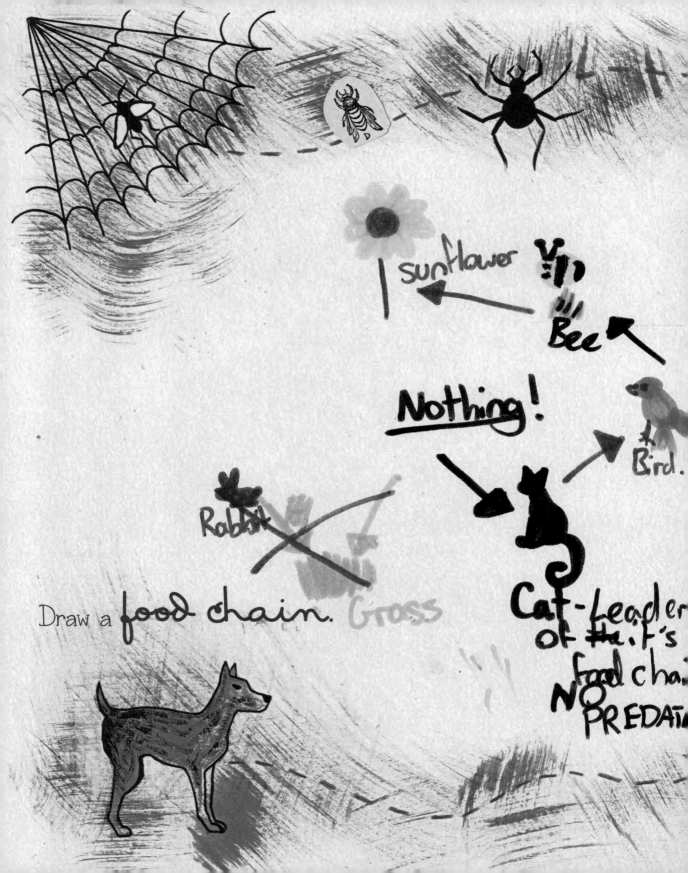

sunflower

Bee

Nothing!

Bird.

Rabbit

Draw a food chain. Gross

Cat - Leader of the it's food chain NO PREDATOR

Draw someone you
WANT TO MEET.

Emma watson

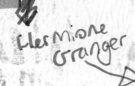

Hermione Granger

Her Majesty
J K Rowling

Adam

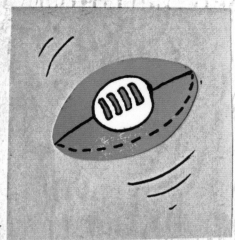

Draw your *favourite* **place.**

Draw your **least** *favourite* **place**.

Draw a **cat** trying to catch a *fish*.

INSPIRATION IS EVERYWHERE.

Draw a *rainbow* in this night sky.

Shade this pattern using a single colour.

Fill this page with **X**s.

Can you transform those Xs into *birds*?

Add BODIES to these tails.

Look around you and draw
everything that is *yellow*.

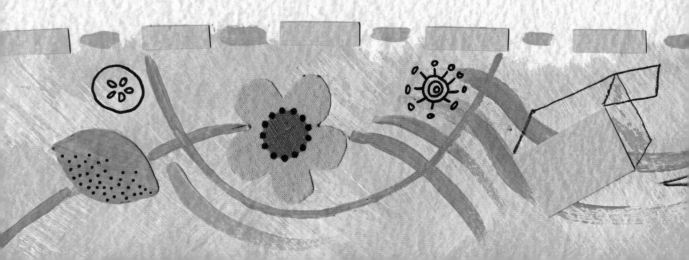

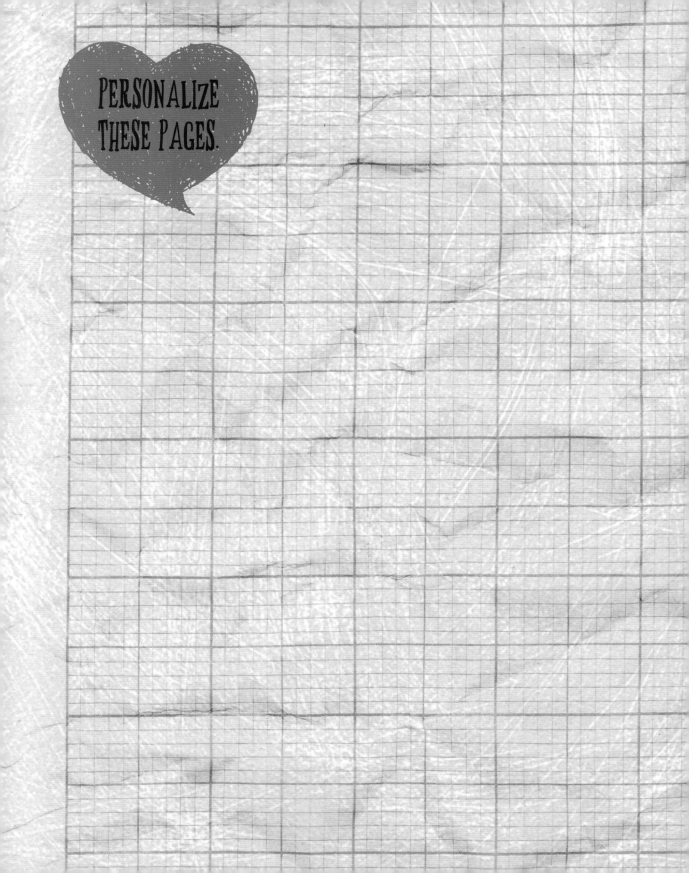

PERSONALIZE
THESE PAGES.

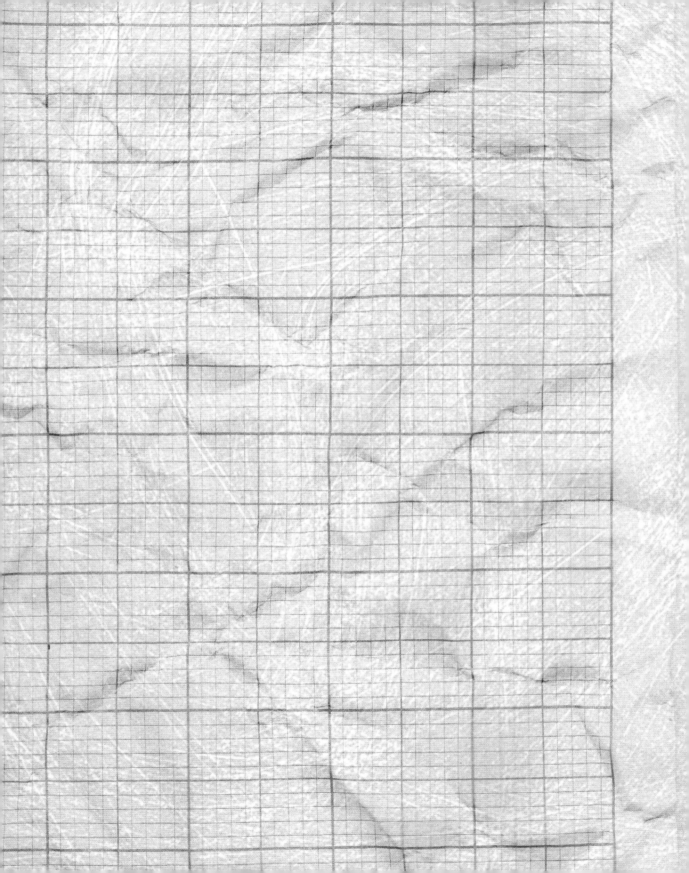

Draw your favourite **quotation.**

I often give myself ve[ry]
follow it.

Alice, Alice in Wonderland
by Lewis Carrol

good advice, but I very seldom

Draw what is under this *magnifying glass.*

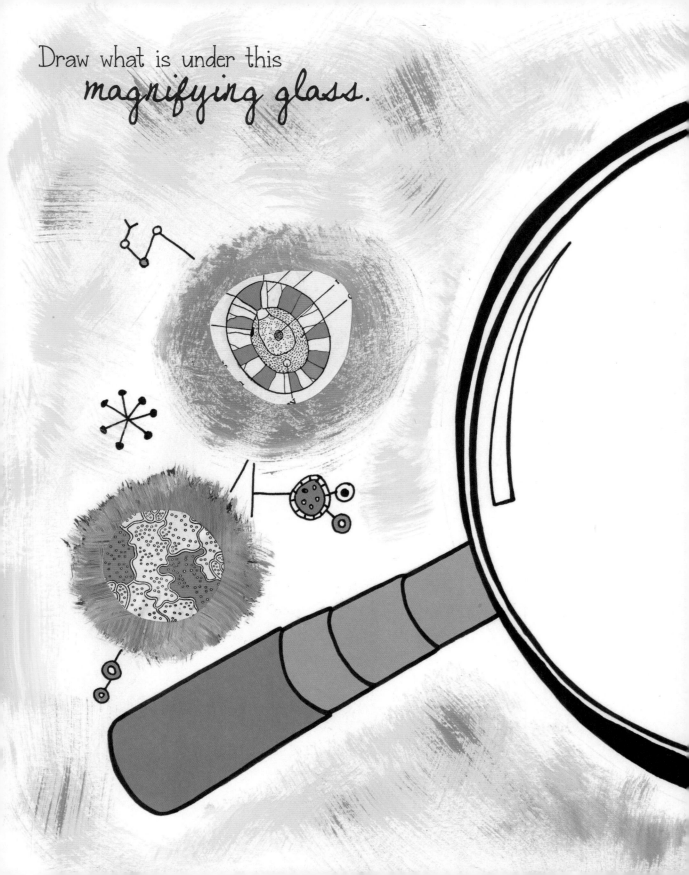

Draw something BRAVE.

Draw something
cowardly.

'ART IS
NOT WHAT YOU
SEE, BUT WHAT
YOU MAKE
OTHERS SEE.'

Edgar Degas